Golf Addicts Galore

Also by George Houghton:

Confessions of a Golf Addict
Golfers A.B.C. (in collaboration)
More Confessions of a Golf Addict
Golf Addict Visits the U.S.A.
Golf Addicts Through the Ages
The Truth About Golf Addicts
Confessions of a Golf Addict
(an anthology from the above titles)
Golf on my Pillow
An Addict's Guide to British Golf
Golf Addicts on Parade
Portrait of a Golf Addict
I am a Golf Widow
Addict in Bunderland
Golf Addict Strikes Again!
Golfers Treasury
Golf—Right from the Start (with Max Faulkner)
The Secret Diary of a Golf Addict's Caddie
Golf Addict Among the Irish
The Full Confessions of a Golf Addict
Golf Addicts Omnibus
Portrait of a Golf Addict (anthology)
Golf no Shinri (in Japanese)
Golf Addict Goes East
Better Golf—Definitely! (with Jessie Valentine)
Golf Addict among the Scots

"THE PURISTS WONT LIKE THIS WAY OF DECLARING US OFFICIALLY OPEN..."

Golf Addicts Galore

Cartoons by

George Houghton

with a Foreword by

RONNIE SHADE, M.B.E.

COUNTRY LIFE BOOKS

First published in 1968
for Country Life Books
by the Hamlyn Publishing Group Limited
Hamlyn House, Feltham, Middlesex
Printed in Great Britain by
Lowe and Brydone (Printers) Ltd London

Foreword

BY RONNIE SHADE, M.B.E.

I can't imagine footballers laughing at their own antics, although goodness knows some are funny enough—particularly when a big brawny chap who has scored a goal is cuddled and kissed by his team mates!

In fact, you seldom hear laughter from games players. Excepting when the game happens to be golf.

I suppose we can laugh at ourselves because we know that when the bug really bites, some aspects of our addiction are unbelievably funny. But we would hate to have golf changed. We like the game as it stands and no keen player wants to see a cooling off in the enthusiasm which often goes to amusing extremes.

A golfer gets saturated, and through the rain he comments: 'We've had the best of the day!'

Considered afterwards, the remark is amusing, yet it is the kind of thing that any of us could say, in dead seriousness.

George Houghton always seems to be hanging around to jot down these things, and the fun of his cartoons is that every golfer can recognise himself. We are all included in Houghton's golfing scenes. He depicts the asides of the game with accuracy because he himself is a dyed-in-the-wool addict. His ideas are not contrived; often they are snatches of conversation which could only have been said by golfers, and possibly they don't raise even the flicker of a smile from the non-golfing Philistines.

A malicious greenkeeper who was sacked, had his revenge on the golf club by filling two holes with bird seed! Hundreds of birds congregated for the tasty meals, news of which no doubt circulated throughout the bird kingdom. This true incident gave Houghton a subject for an amusing drawing, although I don't suppose the club secretary did much laughing!

Golf Addicts Galore

The drawings in *Golf Addicts Galore* have been selected from recent years of the George Houghton annual cartoon calendar, and it is splendid that they should be offered in this permanent form.

Nothing is so transient as a smile, but smiles and even good belly laughter can be re-kindled. That is what happens with golf-addict cartoons, and if they help us to laugh at ourselves they must be good.

We must never get snooty about golf. As Bernard Darwin, echoing his beloved Sam Weller, constantly reminded us 'ours is a werry 'umbling game'.

Ronnie Shade

RONNIE SHADE, M.B.E.

Ronnie David Bell Mitchell Shade has been described as the best amateur golfer Scotland has ever produced. He is the only player to win his national championship four consecutive years and, until the time of writing, has been first choice annually for the Scottish team eight times.

Shade's best year to date was 1966, when, in addition to being the leading amateur in the British Open (he was beaten by only two 'home' professionals), and runner-up in the British Amateur Championship, he returned the best individual score for the Eisenhower Trophy at Mexico City. This 283 was a better total than any professional's on the same course for the Canada Cup in 1958.

Ronnie Shade is the son of a professional golfer. He was born near Edinburgh in 1938 and was christened 'Ronnie'.

'Anything Awful Makes Me Laugh . . .'

That was written by Charles Lamb when he was describing Hazlitt's marriage. He was not thinking of golf. Never mind, it fits, and if anyone can show me life in a more uproarious mood than our first tee on a Sabbath I shall be grateful.

Putting laughter into squiggly lines is never easy and I am not the first to produce humour that is sometimes sombre. Lafevre, the French cartoonist, once clutched an editor by the throat, shook him and said: 'By God, you'll laugh at my jokes or die in the attempt!'

We all have different methods. I would never get away with violence, so this new selection of cartoons is offered with my silent prayer that your putts are currently dropping and your mood is generous, warm and receptive.

I churn out about three hundred golf cartoons a year for my addict books, calendars, Christmas cards, magazine articles, ash trays, tea cloths, tiles, advertisements, and for the folk who actually live with them, framed on the walls of homes and golf clubs.

Ideas and drawings seldom come easy for me. However, compared with operating an electric road-drill, adding up figures, or cleaning windows in frosty weather, my job is a pushover. When a cartoon is finished I pass it to my wife who corrects the spelling in the caption. Sometimes, she reads aloud and says: 'Is that funny?' Then I know it isn't, feel like strangling her, and start again.

My drawings take anything from fifteen minutes to two hours, but often I have scrubbed away with india rubber and razor blade for a whole morning before getting what I want. Usually there is trouble with the expression in a face, or the contortion of a body, but often the idea is a dead loss from the start and simply will not illustrate.

The gag must always be pictorial. When the brawny Jack Nicklaus complained that his legs simply would not stand up to thirty-six holes of golf in a day, a pal of mine said: 'We can't play like the Yanks, but thank goodness we all have lovely legs!' That was a funny remark, but not for a cartoon.

The best ideas are snapped up straight from the golf course, and the man who utters the magic seldom realises he is helping to earn my living. An opponent once holed a long putt, smirked like a cat who has stolen the milk, then trotted up to pluck his ball from the can. A greenkeeper, pausing while bunker-raking, said: 'There goes a contented customer!' That made a cartoon which was reprinted in many journals.

Morsels of home truth are favourites and usually ring the bell when I get the drawing right. Contrived efforts, no matter how ludicrous the situation, seldom come off, simply because the reader cannot identify himself in the situation.

Cartoons for books or calendars must never be topical because nowadays production rushes through like a tortoise. Never, unless he works for a newspaper, must the cartoonist get involved with trends or fashions. My lesson was learnt early on. I had a picture of a locker room. A golfer said 'It helps his putting' and pointed at a man wearing a Davy Crockett fur hat. The picture was funny enough, but although thousands of school kids were then wearing rabbit-skin hats with tails, by the time the cartoon was published, Davy Crockett ideas were in Davy Jones's locker, dead as the dodo.

Each August I deliver to my publisher twenty-six cartoons for the Golf Addicts' Calendar of two years ahead. Only twenty-four drawings are needed, but I supply a couple of extras to allow for duds. Then I crawl off to my London club, knock back a whisky, and heave with relief. To produce the last batch, my ideas barrel has been thoroughly scraped. No longer have I a single golf smile to dispense. Finally, inevitably, I have dried up and this must be the end. That is exactly how I always feel, yet, next day, usually on the golf course, some angel presents me with a pearl which I jot down—and off we go again.

Nothing but golf works for me. Following a publisher's suggestion that I should go for a bigger market, I got cracking on humour books about motoring and gardening. But the subjects soon soured, so now I stick to golf. Of course, writing and drawing about the game are secondary. I am a golf addict first and this may be the reason my work gets by without ulcers.

About ideas, there is nothing new under the sun. Looking through ancient journals in my dentist's waiting room, I have seen jokes which I believed had been born in my own little brain. Yet, on the other hand, old material of mine often crops up over a strange signature. Sometimes the gag has had a fresh coat of paint and this makes me wonder why I didn't give the incident that twist. Often, even while looking at the old drawing, another angle is suggested and once more we're in business.

Cartoon books need good selling titles. Although you may not realise it, lucre is behind even this light-hearted caprice. Titles must give a warm blanket coverage of the contents; also (according to book publishers) the line on the jacket must be simple and somewhat pithy. Latin quips, doubles entendres, and high-falutin' epigrams are a dead loss, commercially.

In my titles, we always include 'golf addict' so that the reader (or buyer) knows there is something rum about the book. No-one can deny that the title for this collection of cartoons is highly appropriate. Each page concerns at least one golf addict, and this, of course, applies to Ronnie Shade, who kindly supplied the Foreword. Thank you, Ronnie, and may you swing away with continuing success.

We live in a swinging world and I hope, kind reader, you find these efforts lighten the scene.

George Houghton

Worthing

"NOW, ALEC, SUPPOSE WE AGREE AT THE START NOT TO SAY 'BAD LUCK' WHEN WE REALLY MEAN 'HOORAY'..."

"I'M REALLY LOOKING FOR A SWING WHICH WILL THRIVE ON NEGLECT"

" WE'VE JUST HAD OUR FIRST QUARREL "

"I'M FED UP WITH ALL THIS TALK OF THE LARGER AMERICAN BALL"
— WE WANT A LARGER **HOLE**!

"— ABOUT THAT JUMBLE SALE ...."

"IT ONCE GOT SO ROUGH WE HAD TO LASH OURSELVES TO TREES . . ."

" YOUNG BARTLETT'S FIANCEE IS MAKING HIS GOLF INCREASINGLY DIFFICULT ! "

"IF YOU'LL PROMISE NOT TO SNEEZE WHEN I'M DRIVING I'LL CUT OUT THE HICCUPPING AS YOU PUTT"

"AH! CIVILIZATION!"

"ANYTHING GOING, FRED'S ALWAYS THERE!"

"NERO HAD HIS FIDDLE, DRAKE HIS BOWLS,
I HAVE MY GOLF... CLEAR?"

"EDGAR IS GETTING FAR TOO EDGY..."

" GOSH ! – I'M EVEN SLICING IN MY DREAMS ! "

"THERE ARE TWO QUESTIONS, AS I SEE IT, —ONE, WHAT CLUB WILL YOU USE?, TWO, IS IT WORTH BREAKING YOUR NECK?.."

"THE NATIVES SEEM RESTLESS TO-DAY"

"IT MAY HELP YOUR PUTTING CONCENTRATION
BUT IT'S NOT DOING ANY GOOD TO THE WALL-PAPER!"

"NOW, LET'S TALK ABOUT **YOU** – WHAT DO YOU THINK OF MY SHORTENED SWING?"

"WITH A TEMPER LIKE THAT IT'S A WONDER THE REF DOESN'T SEND HIM OFF!"

" O BOY! WHAT A CHALLENGE FOR MY ACCOUNTANT!"

"ONCE UPON A TIME, THERE
WAS A WELSH WIZARD –
HIS NAME WAS DAI REES..."

"O BOY! AM I GLAD TO SEE YOU"

" THERE HE GOES AGAIN! THROWING UP GRASS TO CHECK THE WIND... —I DON'T THINK ! "

" BUY THAT ONE, SIR, AND IF IT DOESN'T HIT 'EM TWO HUNDRED YARDS I'LL SEE YOU GET ANOTHER BALL—FREE"

"THERE HE GOES AGAIN! —PLAYING TO THE GALLERY"

"THREE EGGS AND MY DUNLOP 65!"

KEEP YOUR HEAD DOWN

"MOST ATTRACTIVE HOLE ON THE COURSE...
—THE WOODS ARE FULL OF GOLF BALLS!"

" —WHAT COULD BE NICER, SAID YOU, THAN A PENTHOUSE WHERE WE CAN JUST SIT AND SUNBATHE..."

"TOO WET FOR GOLF? THAT'S A COWARDLY THOUGHT—WAS IT TOO WET FOR WELLINGTON TO WIN THE BATTLE OF WATERLOO?"

"OKAY, OKAY, I KNOW IT'S DOWNHILL, I KNOW THERE'S BORROW FROM THE RIGHT— I ALSO KNOW THAT THIS PUTT IS A DARNED SIGHT HARDER SINCE YOU STARTED YAPPING!"

"WILL YOU PLEASE THROW ANOTHER CLUB FOR THE DAILY ECHO?"

"SO YOU BROKE A HUNDRED! — WATCH ME SWELL WITH PRIDE"

"I THINK THAT I SHALL NEVER SEE
A POEM LOVELY AS A TREE...."

"HE'S STILL ON ABOUT HIS FOUR AT THE FIFTH!"

"—THEN, GRADUALLY I DEVELOPED A WIDER ARC..."

"GRIGSBY – REMEMBER ME? THINK BACK TO GORSE HEATH ... 1924 ... BOYS' CHAMPIONSHIP ..."

"WE MUST NOW ASK OURSELVES 'DO WE REALLY DESERVE NICE COOLING DRINKS?'...."

"I KNOW, I KNOW... WE'LL WALK THROUGH LIFE TOGETHER AS PARTNERS... ME CADDYING!"

"ONE LUMP ONLY, MY DEAR"

"I WAS LEADING, THEN HE SLIPPED IN A COUPLE OF QUICK SEVENS..."

"I THINK MY BALL IS TRYING TO SAY SOMETHING!"

"NOT A WORD DEAR, PLEASH-H, OR YOU'LL SHPOIL THE BESHT ROUND OF MY LIFE ...."

"HERE'S A COURSE THAT SEPARATES THE MEN FROM THE BOYS ... !"

"YOU MIGHT TRY CHALKING YOUR CLUBHEAD"

"NEXT TIME YOU WALK ROUND, FOR PETE'S SAKE DON'T WEAR STILETTO HEELS!"

"APART FROM GOLF, HOW'S LIFE TREATING YOU?"

"THAT'LL STOP 'EM FLUKING IT UP TO THE GREEN!"

"NOW THAT I CAN AFFORD TO BUY GOLF BALLS I CAN'T HIT THEM FAR ENOUGH TO LOSE 'EM!"

E

"YOU DON'T OFTEN FIND A GREENKEEPER AS CONSCIENTIOUS AS OLD FRED"

"THERE GOES ONE OF GOLF'S FRINGE BENEFITS"

"SOMEONE MUST TELL THE SKIPPER ABOUT PRACTICE SWINGS ON THE TEE"

"SO YOU'RE BACK! — NO, DON'T TELL ME — I KNOW... THE PUTTS WOULDN'T DROP... YOU SLICED OUT OF BOUNDS AT THE THIRD...."

"AUBREY PLAYS IN THE LOW 70's — IF IT GETS COLDER HE GOES IN!"

"THE FIRST CAN BE REGARDED AS A PRACTICE SWING!"

"READY, JOHNNY BOY? —DON'T MAKE ANY PROMISES ABOUT WHEN WE'LL BE BACK!"

"AND TO THINK THAT I COULD
HAVE BEEN PEACEFULLY LOSING
MONEY AT CLUBHOUSE BRIDGE!"

"LET'S RUN THROUGH IT AGAIN — EYE ON THE BALL, FULL SHOULDER PIVOT, LEFT ARM NICE AND STRAIGHT, HEAD STILL, TO HELL WITH THE OFFICE ... "

"BE HAPPY FOR THE LAWN"

"MEAT BALLS, MEAT BALLS, ALWAYS MEAT BALLS... WHY CAN'T CHEF DO HIS PUTTING SOMEWHERE ELSE?"

"SOMETIMES HE PUTS TOO MUCH STOP ON IT"

" IT DOESN'T SAY ANYTHING IN THE GUIDE BOOK ABOUT BEING BUILT THE YEAR MAX FAULKNER WON THE OPEN!"

"THE FIRST THING IS LEARNING TO BALANCE THE BALL ON THE TEE"

"MOST MEN IN HAWAII FOR THE FIRST TIME WOULD BE INTERESTED IN MORE THAN JUST GOLF AND SAM SNEAD HATS!"

"I HATE GIMMICKS!"

"—SO PLEASE DON'T ADJUST YOUR SET"

"COULD WE DISCUSS LESSONS IN TERMS OF A BLOCK BOOKING?"

"FORE!"

"I TOLD HER IT WAS A MISTAKE TO GET MARRIED ON MONTHLY MEDAL DAY"

" PLAYING SAFE, EH ? "

"CUT OUT THAT SIR GALAHAD STUFF! —GIVING TEN INCH PUTTS!!!..."

"IN FUTURE, I'LL PUT YOUR TROUSERS AWAY!"

" FOR TEN YEARS THE GOLF CLUB WAS MY GREATEST JOY — THEN I BECAME A PLAYING MEMBER ... "

" I'LL NEVER FORGIVE YOU FOR THIS, ALICE — NOR WILL THE COMMITTEE ! "

"WHICH OF YOU NOTICED MY DELIBERATE MISTAKE?"

"—AND I SAY IT WAS SHORTER THAN THE PUTT YOU MISSED AT THE 6th! —YOU TRYING TO START SOMETHING, FORBES?"

"AH WELL, WE ALL HAVE OUR SIMPLE PLEASURES"

"SSH—SH—SH!"

"SAY WHAT YOU LIKE, ALL I CAN HEAR
IS A SMALL VOICE WHISPERING –
'YOU'RE GOING TO FLUFF IT'..."

"CHIPPING PRACTICE FOR ANOTHER HALF HOUR, THEN DOWN WE GO FOR THE WORMS"

" COME NOW, MRS. PILKINGTON, YOU'RE TOO EASILY DISCOURAGED... "

"THE DIFFERENCE BETWEEN YOUR GOLF AND MINE IS THAT ONE BAD SHOT RUINS YOUR DAY AND ONE GOOD SHOT MAKES MINE!"

"CARPET PUTTING WILL DO FOR MOST GOLFERS —
<u>OUR</u> DRAWING-ROOM MUST BE A TIGER COURSE!"

"CAN THIS BE THE SAME CONFIDENT CAREFREE HUSBAND WHO ONLY AT BREAKFAST TOLD ME HE HAD COMPLETELY MASTERED THE PALMER METHOD?"

"—AND THE MAIN THING IS TO BE RELAXED AND ABSOLUTELY FREE..."

"CAN YOU MANAGE A LITTLE SMILE?"

"HE'S BROKEN THE COURSE RECORD!
— FIVE PUTTS AT THE SIXTEENTH!"

" TRUST JENKINSON TO MAKE AN ENTRANCE ON THE FIRST TEE ! "

"COME, GILFILLAN, YOU CAN'T MIX GOLF WITH THE MAD SOCIAL WHIRL"

"HE'S TRYING OUT AN OVERLAP GRIP"

"DAD, CAN I BORROW A COUPLE OF DECENT GOLF BALLS — AND YOUR HOLE-IN-ONE TIE?"

"WHEN I SAY LUNCH AT ONE O'CLOCK
I MEAN LUNCH AT ONE O'CLOCK!"

"I HAVE A FEELING THAT YOUR FRIENDS WOULD RATHER BE SOMEWHERE ELSE..."

"GOSH! HAVE YOU EVER SEEN A BALL WITH SUCH A SENSE OF HUMOUR!"

"THERE Y'ARE! I KEPT MY HEAD DOWN LIKE *YOU* SAID AND I FLUFFED IT AGAIN—LIKE *I* SAID!"

"IT'S ALWAYS THE SAME, FRED—YOU NEVER KNOW WHEN A DAY'S GOLF IS OVER, DO YOU?"